MAJOR PEST CONTROL

STORIES
FROM THE TRENCHES
A HOMEOWNER'S GUIDE
TO PEST CONTROL

JUN BUKHT
ASSOCIATE CERTIFIED ENTOMOLOGIST

Jun Bukht -- 1st ed.

ISBN: 978-1-954757-26-4

The publisher has strived to be as accurate and complete as possible in the creation of this book.

This book is not intended for use as a legal, business, accounting, or financial advice source. All readers are advised to seek the services of competent professionals in the legal, business, accounting, and finance fields.

Like anything else in life, there are no guarantees of income or results in practical advice books. Readers are cautioned to rely on their own judgment about their individual circumstances to act accordingly.

While all attempts have been made to verify the information provided in this publication, the publisher assumes no responsibility for errors, omissions, or contrary interpretation of the subject matter herein. Any perceived slights of specific persons, peoples, or organizations are unintentional.

CONTENTS

INTRODUCTION

I wrote this book with every homeowner in mind. Most of us have experienced the unsettling feeling of watching an army of ants parade across our kitchen or a mysterious multi-legged creature climbing the walls just after dark. You might consult the internet for advice on what to do in these situations, but most stories and information are grossly exaggerated or completely false. My goal is to provide you with peace of mind by having this book in your home to give you accurate answers to your questions whenever you might need it.

I will cover the 15 most common pests that people in North America encounter in and around their homes. There isn't another resource out there that gives you all of this information in one place, and since Major Pest Control can't be at your beck and call 24/7, this book is the next best thing.

You may be wondering why I'm the guy to advise you on pesky critters. It all started about twelve years ago with a story I like to refer to as "The Haunted Hotel." This story awaits you in Chapter One, and unfortunately, my family was a victim of one of the most dreaded bugs in existence. From that moment on, I declared war on these particular bugs and every other pest that could have such adverse physical and emotional effects on a family. Pests carry diseases, cause fire hazards through chewed wires, and contaminate food with bacteria. Often, people are unaware of just how dangerous even the smallest pests can be once they find their way into your home. Allow me to help your family effectively identify, deal with, and ultimately eliminate pests from your life.

—Jun Bukht, Associate Certified Entomologist

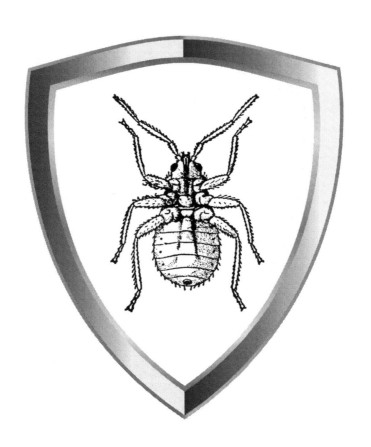

CHAPTER ONE

THE HAUNTED HOTEL

It all started about twelve years ago when I stayed in a hotel with my wife and ten-month-old son. The hotel was clean, comfortable, and recently renovated. To our dismay, we woke up the following day to find a rash all over our son's body. We attempted to problem-solve with the hotel staff, changing out bed sheets and pillowcases if it was a detergent or feather allergy. The doctor prescribed a rash ointment when we returned home, but the rash would not go away. As any panicked parent would, we started posting pictures on social media and asking for input on what this could be. A friend of mine who worked for a pest control company mentioned bed bug bites. He offered to inspect our house, at which point he discovered we had brought bed bugs from the hotel into our home. It was a nightmare. After a month-long battle and treatment regimen, our house was finally bed bug-free.

WHAT IS A BED BUG?

Bed bugs (Cimex sp.) are common household pests. As parasitic insects, they must live near their hosts. Given humans are bed bugs' hosts, bed bugs live in homes, hotels, and other structures where humans are regularly found. Their needs are minimal, requiring only a safe area near their human hosts. Bed bugs quickly move to bite the exposed skin of sleeping humans and then return to their hideout following their blood meal. Despite their small size, bed bugs can travel farther than three meters from their shelter to take a blood meal, but are more commonly found near their host, usually one to two meters.

DETECTION AND IDENTIFICATION

Bed bugs are easily overlooked unless you have learned to identify them with key features. Adults are 4 to 5 mm long, reddish-brown, oval-shaped with flattened bodies, and have two antennae and six legs. The abdomen of bed bugs is darker in color after a blood meal. Their flattened bodies allow them to hide in small places like bed frames, sofas, behind loose wallpaper, under carpets, in baseboards or cracks in floors, and behind picture frames and other areas that make them challenging to observe. Bed bugs hang out close to one another, thus resulting in a large population that will emit an unpleasant, sweet odor.

THE LIFESTYLE OF BED BUGS

Bed bugs are attracted to humans because of the carbon dioxide and warmth we produce. They primarily infest multi-unit buildings, like hotels and apartments, which experience high turnover and where they are frequently introduced by luggage or used furniture. Bed bugs are hitchhikers that hide in people's belongings, like purses, briefcases, and laptop bags; they don't actually cling to people. Once hidden within belongings, they are quickly introduced to homes, offices, hospitals, and other structures. Additionally, bed bugs can infest various modes of transportation. Unlike many other pests, proper hygiene does not prevent bed bug infestations.

SIGNS OF BED BUG INFESTATION

To detect bed bug activity, inspect bedding, mattresses, and box springs for living or dead insects, molted skins, and small reddish-black spots of fecal matter. Bed bugs also lay their eggs (0.8 to 3 mm in size) in small cracks and crevices near where they feed. Frequently, bed bug bites go unnoticed or are misdiagnosed.

SPREADING OF BED BUGS

Bed bugs tend to stay in areas where they have become established, but they may also be spread due to several scenarios. Bed bugs may spread due to disturbances, such as removing furniture or incorrectly applying pesticides. When they experience a food shortage, bed bugs may migrate to neighboring rooms, searching for suitable hosts. Likewise, a lack of appropriate sheltering areas may result in bed bugs migrating to other rooms. Bed bugs can also be spread through many human activities, such as using the same vacuum cleaner in multiple rooms, moving infested furniture within the home, or passing it on to others.

AFTER DETECTION

Upon detecting bed bug activity, leave the room and do not further disturb the contents. Make sure not to take any items out of the infested room, as that may contribute to allowing the bed bugs to spread further. Immediately contact a trusted professional pest control company. The pest control company will inspect the premises and advise on pre-treatment procedures.

LIFE CYCLE OF BED BUGS

Bed bug infestations require the services of a professional pest control company because their life cycle makes them extremely difficult to eradicate. Females lay up to 500 eggs in their lifetime, in clutches of 10 to 50 eggs at a time. After six to 17 days of development, the eggs hatch, and the nymphs are released. These nymphs look like miniature versions of adults and will undergo several molts to become adults. Adult bed bugs can survive more than one year between blood meals.

- ✓ Eliminate clutter from around the home.
- ✓ Vacuum frequently to remove bed bugs that may have hitchhiked into the home.
- ✓ Wash and dry bedding at the hottest temperatures the fabric can withstand.
- ✓ Encase mattresses and box springs in a high-quality protective cover resistant to tearing. Regularly inspect the cover for any holes.
- ✓ Use care when bringing second-hand furniture into the home.
- ✓ Avoid bringing discarded furniture into the home; it was disposed of for a reason.
- ✓ Regularly inspect your home: after moving in, after traveling, after a service call by a technician, or after overnight guests.
- ✓ If living in a multi-family home, isolate your unit by installing door sweeps and sealing cracks and crevices along baseboards, light sockets, etc.
- ✓ Exercise vigilance when using shared laundry facilities.
- ✓ Use covers on power outlets.
- ✓ Store clothing in vacuum-sealed bags when traveling.
- ✓ Inspect pet bedding.
- ✓ Avoid using moving blankets provided by a moving company.

- ✓ Examine second-hand items, even products that look harmless like electronics which often have vents in which bed bugs can hide.
- ✓ Beware of bed bugs in public places such as store dressing rooms, where bed bugs can hide in the cushioned seats and carpeted floors.

Q: How do I know if I have a bed bug bite?

A: Everyone reacts differently to bed bug bites. Some people who are bitten will not react. Others experience raised reddish welts that are itchy and around 0.5 to 1 cm in diameter. Multiple bites are often clustered near each other in groups of two to three. It is important to note that many other insect bites can result in similar welts, so the bites themselves are not diagnostic without other direct evidence of bed bug activity.

Q: Are bed bug bites harmful or contagious?

A: While some people experience pain from bed bug bites, others do not. A bite can be harmful if it develops blisters or welts. Welts may develop into a more serious secondary infection that may include pain, significant inflammation, and swelling. While bed bug bites create some health risks, they are not contagious.

• • •

Once you have properly identified a bed bug infestation, promptly contact a professional pest control company. A small problem quickly becomes a large infestation as bed bugs can lay up to ten eggs a day. Take action to protect yourself and your loved ones from being "haunted" while you sleep.

CHAPTER TWO

———◆———

DO YOU EVER WONDER WHAT'S "BUGGING" YOUR MOTHER-IN-LAW?

One evening, my mother-in-law, an excellent cook, had just finished serving us a delicious meal. As I was helping her clean the kitchen, I noticed a small bug scampering across the floor. I immediately identified it as a German cockroach. When I approached my mother-in-law about it, she said, "I don't have cockroaches! Cockroaches are *big*! These are tiny, and they are everywhere in the house. When I spray them, they disappear for a week and then slowly start to come back out again. I don't see them during the day; they just come out at night."

It is a common misconception that all cockroaches are large in size. This chapter will discuss what I wish my mother-in-law would have known about her tiny kitchen invaders.

WHAT IS A COCKROACH?

While more than 4,500 cockroach species are found globally, fewer than 50 are considered pest species that invade homes and other structures. The most common cockroach species is the German cockroach. Several other structure-infesting cockroaches exist, including the American cockroach, Oriental cockroach, Brown-banded cockroach, and Wood cockroach.

Cockroaches are among the most adaptable insects known and can persist in any location that provides enough food, moisture, and heat. Cockroaches frequently invade homes and other structures in search of favorable habitats: those that are warm and damp and near food and water sources. They commonly reside in basements, bathrooms, kitchens, greenhouses, or other rooms with plumbing pipes. Cockroaches tend to be nocturnal, hide during the day, and are active at night. They rapidly flee when disturbed and easily travel between rooms.

THE COCKROACH DIET

Cockroaches are omnivorous (they can eat nearly anything) and feed upon various scavenged foods. They typically feed on dead or decaying vegetation or other organic matter when living outdoors. When living indoors, cockroaches will feed on multiple items used by humans, including everyday pantry items, leather, fabric, glue, soap, and toothpaste. Cockroaches tend to be attracted to substances high in sugar or starch. Cockroaches can persist for weeks in the absence of food or water.

THE LIFE CYCLE OF A COCKROACH

Typically, cockroaches live up to one year. During their lifetimes, female cockroaches may produce 100 to 200 eggs. These eggs are produced in a protective egg case that female cockroaches deposit in discreet locations. However, some cockroach species carry the egg case until the eggs are ready to hatch. Eggs incubate for 20 to 60 days before hatching. When the eggs hatch, the nymphs are released. Nymphs undergo a process called metamorphosis that transforms their bodies. As nymphs grow, they must molt their skins several times to develop into adults. The stages between each molt are called instar stages, and most cockroaches go through six or seven instar stages before becoming adults. A cockroach completes its life cycle within two months to a year. The length of time it takes for a cockroach to develop from an egg into an adult is influenced by environmental factors such as temperature and humidity.

THE GERMAN COCKROACH

The scientific name of the German cockroach is Blattella germanica. Adults are 13 to 16 mm long, while immature cockroaches may be a few millimeters long. They are light brown to tan in color, have elongated, wide, flattened bodies, possess six legs and two long antennae, and cannot fly. As omnivorous scavengers, German cockroaches feed on nearly anything but prefer foods with a high content of sugar, starch, or oils. Within homes and other structures, German cockroaches infest areas that provide food, moisture, and warmth sources, such as within and around household appliances, kitchens, bathrooms, under sinks, dishwashers, pantries, storage closets, and medicine cabinets.

COCKROACH PREVENTION TIPS

- ✓ Store food, including pet food, in tightly sealed containers.
- ✓ Put pet water dishes away when not in use.
- ✓ Keep the home clean and tidy.
- ✓ Store garbage containers in dry areas outside the kitchen.
- ✓ Promptly clean up spills.
- ✓ Remove stored cardboard, grocery bags, newspapers, and magazines.
- ✓ Use caulk to seal all cracks and crevices that can be used to enter the home.
- ✓ Vacuum regularly.
- ✓ Remove garbage daily.
- ✓ Wash and put away dishes.
- ✓ Repair any plumbing leaks to eliminate any sources of moisture.
- ✓ Use garbage cans with tightly sealed lids.
- ✓ Use liners in all garbage cans.
- ✓ Sweep and mop around and under kitchen appliances and household furniture.
- ✓ Inspect incoming packages for cockroach droppings and egg casings.
- ✓ Ensure vents, windows, and screens are in good repair and seal tightly.
- ✓ Install weather stripping and door sweeps around exterior doors.

Q: Do cockroaches fly?

A: The majority of cockroach species can fly. The German cockroach possesses wings but does not fly, instead does short downward gliding. Other cockroach species may be able to fly for short distances, such as Brown-banded cockroaches and wood cockroaches. While some cockroaches possess varying degrees of flying capabilities, cockroaches are better adapted to running than flying.

Q: How worried should I be about cockroaches?

A: Cockroach infestations create unsanitary conditions that can pose threats to human health. Consuming cockroach-contaminated foods may cause food poisoning, while exposure to cockroach feces is linked to adverse health effects, especially in asthma patients. As cockroaches crawl through garbage and sewers and onto kitchen countertops, they may spread harmful bacteria such as coliforms, Salmonella, Staphylococcus, and Streptococcus. Once cockroaches have invaded the home, elimination is highly challenging. They can survive in the absence of food and water. Cockroach eggs are protected from insecticides by an egg case, which means that even when you kill adults, newly hatched cockroaches are ready to replace them. The only way to eradicate a cockroach infestation is by employing a trusted and reputable professional pest control company.

Q: Do cockroaches cause allergies?

A: Many individuals have immune systems that react to harmless substances such as pollen and dust. It has been documented that cockroaches trigger allergic responses in around 12% of the population with no other allergies. Roughly 33% of individuals sensitive to other allergens also experience allergic reactions due to cockroaches. Sensitive individuals may be triggered to have allergic reactions when exposed to cockroach feces, saliva, dead bodies, and molted skins. These allergens may become particulate and airborne within the home, potentially irritating the respiratory systems of people who live in or visit the house. Allergic reactions from cockroach exposure may manifest as sinus congestion, rashes, sore throats, and eye irritation. If allergic symptoms are experienced year-round, this may indicate cockroach infestation, given that most allergies are seasonal. Additionally, allergic reactions to cockroaches may aggravate asthma conditions in susceptible asthmatics.

Q: Do cockroaches bite?

A: While considered rare and associated with extreme infestations, cockroaches have mouth parts that can bite the flesh of humans and pets. The area around the bite may swell or become red and irritated. As with any insect bite, cockroach bites bear an infection risk. A cockroach bite will increase in size when infected, becoming inflamed and pus-filled. When cockroaches target humans, they typically bite the fingers and skin around the nails.

* * *

In conclusion, as tempting as it may be to try spraying or deep cleaning once you have discovered cockroaches, this will only exacerbate the problem by causing them to scatter to other areas of your home. A professional pest control company can eliminate these uninvited dinner guests and allow your family to focus on delicious, home-cooked meals instead of the bugs darting around at their feet.

CHAPTER THREE

"CAN YOU PRESCRIBE ME SOMETHING FOR...RODENTS?"

Our family doctor called me and said, "I'm hearing noises off and on in the walls and ceilings of my house." Being a successful doctor, he had very little time to investigate on his own and often passed out as soon as he arrived home from work. He rarely went down to the basement, so I decided to look around there first when I arrived at his house. As it turns out, a large, dark, undisturbed basement makes a lovely home for mice. Every box contained nesting material and babies, as mice reproduce rapidly. They made their way into the vents from the ducts and were scampering inside of the walls, creating the sounds the doctor would often hear. This time around, I was the one providing my doctor with a prescription - to get rid of mice!

MICE EXPLAINED

Mice invade many homes and structures. Mice are carriers of disease and can damage property. Deer mice and house mice are the most common species of mice. The most common carrier of the deadly Hantavirus is the deer mouse. Mice are 150 to 170 mm in length, including the tail, are brown or tan, and have oversized ears and long tails. Deer mice's coats are brown or gray, with a white underbelly and feet. House mice have brown or gray fur, lighter-colored fur on their bodies' undersides, and pinkish-buff fur on their feet. The tails of house mice are about the same as their body length, while the tails of deer mice are shorter than their body length.

Mice are secretive and live in habitats that provide complete concealment. When outdoors, mice live in the vegetation and underbrush of grassy fields and farmland. Mice often seek refuge in homes and other structures, from businesses, warehouses, and factories, to dog houses, sheds, garages, outbuildings, and yard decorations. In populated areas, mice live near food sources in areas with a low threat of predation.

WHAT DO MICE EAT?

Mice are omnivores (they can eat nearly anything), including seeds, fruits, nuts, insects, and human-derived foods, such as stored or discarded items. In addition to consuming foods, mice are widely known for chewing and biting through inedible objects, such as papers, books, drywall, plastic, and soft metals like aluminum. Mice require multiple meals daily, with some species feeding up to 30 times in a single day.

THE LIFE CYCLE OF A MOUSE

Mice are mammals, which means they give birth to live young after a gestation period of around 20 days. Mice litters have six to eight pups. Female deer mice and house mice typically produce up to a dozen litters annually. Female pups reach sexual maturity after around one month, while male pups are sexually mature after two months. Early summer to late fall is the prime mating season when mice live outdoors. However, mice that live indoors may reproduce year-round. Mice live for up to two years.

MICE PREVENTION TIPS

- ✓ Keep the kitchen and pantry clean and tidy.
- ✓ Store food items (including pet food) in sturdy plastic or metal containers with tight-fitting lids.
- ✓ Quickly clean up spills and crumbs that could attract rodents or ants.
- ✓ Wash dishes and cooking utensils as soon as possible after use.
- ✓ Don't leave pet food or water bowls out. Always put away pet food after use, clean up uneaten food, and empty water bowls before bed.
- ✓ Position bird feeders away from the home and always use squirrel guards to keep out squirrels and other rodents.
- ✓ Use garbage cans made from thick plastic or metal with tight-fitting lids.
- ✓ Regularly clean the garbage cans with soap and water.
- ✓ Position compost bins at least 100 feet away from the house, but further is better.
- ✓ Seal openings into the structure greater than 6 mm using copper mesh and expanding foam sealant.
- ✓ Discard cardboard after use; do not store it for future uses.
- ✓ Repair any water leaks around pipes or on the roof.
- ✓ Direct rain away from the structure using gutters and downspouts.
- ✓ Remove debris from around the house.
- ✓ Store rock piles or lumber away from the structure.
- ✓ Remain vigilant in watching for signs of infestations and respond promptly.

FAQ

Q: Why do I have mice?

A: Homes and other structures provide many of the requirements mice have for living, such as food and water, warmth, and shelter from predators. They invade seeking these requirements, often responding to falling temperatures that signal the onset of winter. Once inside, mice build nests in undisturbed areas away from light, such as attics, pantries, garages, and within walls. Mice often seek out and invade stored food items within the home. House mice consume various foods, such as fruits, nuts, seeds, insects, grains, discarded foods, and stored pantry items. Deer mice also consume many food sources, such as beetles, earthworms, snails, seeds, fruit, and fungi, and are especially attracted to homes with large insect populations or easily raided pantry items.

Q: Do mice hibernate?

A: Mice do not hibernate. Instead, mice are less active during the winter, tending to stay in the nest to avoid low temperatures. Homes provide excellent refuge for mice, with plenty of warmth, food, and shelter. Mice prefer to nest in vents and other openings that access basements and attics.

Q: How do I tell the difference between deer mice and house mice?

A: Deer mice have brown or gray fur with white bellies and tail bottoms. A deer mouse's tail is approximately the same length as its body. Deer mice have hind legs that are longer than their forelegs. Deer mice have larger eyes and ears than house mice, which is often the most reliable method for differentiating between the two mouse species. House mice typically have gray fur; some have brown shading along their backs or undersides. House mice are about 8 cm in length, have long tails partially covered in fur, and short hind legs.

Q: How worried should I be about mice?

A: Mice are carriers of disease and can damage property. In homes, mice contaminate living areas by depositing feces and urine and tracking around detritus. Deadly Hantavirus, which causes a rare respiratory disease, can be carried and transmitted by deer mice saliva, urine, and feces. Hantavirus may be fatal in humans, and there is no known cure. Hantavirus may be spread due to tiny particles of deer mouse waste circulating in the air. Mice are known to contaminate ten times the amount of food relative to what they consume. This contamination allows for the transmission of diseases and parasites. One mouse-transmitted disease is salmonellosis, resulting in diarrhea, fever, and vomiting. Parasites such as mites and fleas may also cause dermatitis.

Mice also destroy property by biting through or chewing on inedible materials such as books, plastics, aluminum, drywall, insulation, siding, and wallboard, which may compromise the building's structural integrity. The activities of mice in creating nests and food caches may cause small openings in the structure to become progressively wider. Mice may also chew through electrical wiring, causing many problems, from power outages to electrical fires, which are expensive to repair. Businesses, such as restaurants, property management, and hotels, affected by mouse infestations may face disastrous consequences. These establishments face ruined reputations in addition to extensive damage. Homeowners may achieve temporary and sporadic control of mouse infestations using glue or snap traps. However, to achieve the permanent and reliable eradication of mice, homeowners and businesses must employ the services of a trusted and reputable professional pest control company.

* * *

As you can see, mice are destructive, dirty pests that can damage your treasured possessions and spread disease to you and your family. Professional pest control companies have potent prescriptions for curing even the most extreme of mouse misfortunes.

CHAPTER FOUR

BUNGALOW WOES

This is the tale of a retiree named Nancy who lived in a beautiful bungalow. She had always noticed large, black ants in her yard, but they gradually moved closer to her home. She also saw them *inside* her beloved bungalow, with sawdust coming out of the walls. She called me to do an inspection, where I immediately discovered lots of evidence of carpenter ants. They had made a massive nest under her front yard cedar tree, which encompassed almost the entirety of the yard. I also found satellite nests in the backyard and inside of the house. These ants chewed tunnels through the wood and drywall of her home, beginning their mission to destroy the bungalow, little by little, creating extensive structural damage.

ALL ABOUT ANTS

There are several species of ants. Some of these species are "structure-infesting," meaning they have the ability to reside in and around your home. The most common species of structure-infesting ants are carpenter ants, odorous house ants, pavement ants, Argentine ants, Pharaoh ants, acrobat ants, and thief ants. Carpenter ants, pavement ants, and pharaoh ants are responsible for most problems in the home. The species most associated with structural damage is the black carpenter ant, which is also the largest. When nesting indoors, pavement ants tend to be more of an annoyance than a cause of structural damage. Similarly, Pharaoh ants are indoor nuisance pests and are attracted to foods high in protein and sugar.

TYPES OF ANTS

Acrobat Ants

Acrobat ants belong to the genus *Crematogaster*, are less than 5.5 mm in length, have heart-shaped abdomens, and emit an odor when disturbed. When found outside, acrobat ants establish colonies near moisture: under rocks and in rotting wood such as stumps or woodpiles. When infesting indoors, acrobat ants typically nest in moist areas like foam insulation behind siding or where water leaks have damaged the structure.

Argentine Ants

The scientific name for Argentine ants is *Linepithema humile*. They are about 2.5 mm (+/- 3 mm) in length, have smooth, hairless bodies, and are light to dark brown. Argentine ants are found outdoors in soil, under wood and logs, and in the cavities at the base of trees and shrubs. While Argentine ants are omnivorous (they can eat nearly anything), they seek out sweet foods.

Carpenter Ants

Carpenter ants belong to the genus *Camponotus*, are between 3 and 13 mm in length, have a rounded thorax and prominent mandibles, and are brown, black, or red and black in color. Carpenter ants nest both indoors and outdoors in moist, rotting wood. Unlike termites that eat wood, carpenter ants remove wood, depositing the debris in small piles outside their nests.

Fire Ants

Fire ants range from reddish brown to reddish black. They have a stinger that causes sharp pain and burning sensations in unsuspecting victims. The red, itchy welts from the sting can eventually turn into blisters. Fire ants tend to favor sunny areas to build their mounds, which can be as large as 18 cm tall and 61 cm wide. They will likely appear in lawns and fields as fire ants avoid darkness and shade. As colonies increase, they may build additional mounds with new queens. Though they eat insects and dead animals in the wild, fire ants prefer sweets and fats once they have invaded the home.

Odorous House Ants

The scientific name for odorous house ants is *Tapinoma sessile*. They are between 2 and 3 mm long and are dark gray or brown in color. Their name is derived from the rotten odor they emit if crushed. Outdoors, odorous house ants live in shallow nests established on beaches and in swamps and bogs. Indoors, they are attracted to warmth and moisture and will colonize within walls, around hot water pipes and heaters, and under sinks and bathtubs. Odorous house ants are highly opportunistic and are active year-round.

Pavement Ants

The scientific name for pavement ants is *Tetramorium immigrans*. They are between 2.5 and 3 mm in length, have visible grooves on their head and thorax, have one pair of spines on their thorax, and are pale brown to black. Their name is derived from their tendency to establish nests under sidewalks, driveways, and building foundations. A common sign of pavement ant activity is a mound of displaced soil near a paved area. Pavement ants may establish nests.

Pharaoh Ants

The scientific name for pharaoh ants is *Monomorium pharaonis*. Workers are 2 mm in length and yellow to light brown in color, while queens are 4 mm in length and reddish. Queen Pharaoh ants, which are twice the size of workers, have enlarged abdomens that are darker in color than the rest of their bodies. Before mating, queen pharaoh ants have wings that they shed after mating. Pharaoh ants are sometimes overlooked due to their small size and inconspicuous color, allowing them to infest structures. They establish nests in areas with moisture, such as kitchens and bathrooms, and use plumbing pipes and electrical lines within walls to forage in other rooms.

Thief Ants

The scientific name of thief ants is *Solenopsis molesta*. They are also known as "sugar ants" or "grease ants." Workers are 1.5 mm in length (+/- 3 mm), while queens are 6 mm in length. They are yellow to light brown and have two nodes between the thorax and abdomen. Thief ants are commonly mistaken for Pharaoh ants. An important distinguishing feature is the antennae, consisting of 10 segments terminating in a two-segmented club. Their name is derived from their habit of stealing resources and offspring from neighboring colonies. Thief ants forage long distances but are not attracted to sweets. They are resistant to conventional ant traps and most insecticides. For colonies that are established within structures, they may be overlooked for an extended period due to their small size and inconspicuous color.

✓ Promptly clean up food spills.
✓ Use air-tight containers for food storage.
✓ Remove pet dishes and food when not in use.
✓ Seal cracks and crevices.
✓ Repair water leaks.
✓ Trim landscaping to prevent vegetation from touching the home.

Q: Why do I have ants?

A: Many species of ants are foraging ants that travel long distances away from the nest in search of food. They are attracted by food in the home and enter to forage for crumbs and spills or other edible items they may encounter. Ants enter buildings using cracks in walls, foundations, or gaps and small openings where plumbing or electrical lines enter the home. Many ant species can continue infesting once they have gained entry by following an invisible scent trail that scouts produce when searching for food.

Q: What attracts ants to your house?

A: Your home provides the three things ants need: food, moisture, and nesting sites. Ants are attracted to food remnants found within the home, such as spills, crumbs, and leftover pet foods. Ants are also attracted to areas within the home where moisture collects, such as in areas with rain damage, leaky pipes, or other condensation. Finally, ants are attracted to locations within the house suitable for nesting, such as moisture-damaged wood, exposed dirt from cracks and crevices, wall voids, and subflooring.

Q: Can ants build nests in walls?

A: Yes, ants can build nests in your home's walls, mainly if any cracks or crevices are present.

Q: Do ants bite?

A: Several ant species have jaws capable of biting through human skin, although most cannot. Black carpenter ants are known to bite when provoked. Other ant species, such as European fire ants, also inject formic acid into the bite wound, which results in a burning sensation at the wound site.

Q: How do I get rid of an ant nest?

A: Upon discovering an ant nest, you can treat it with an appropriately labeled pesticide that immediately kills all members of the colony (queen(s), workers, pupae, and larvae). If you cannot determine the nest's location, you can use an appropriately labeled ant bait to bait foraging ants. Workers that encounter the bait will take it back to the colony where the other members will eat it, killing all colony members. To achieve elimination, it is imperative to use the correct type of bait consistently.

Q: How do I get rid of ants in my house?

A: Eliminating ants is difficult because ants are social animals with large colonies. The use of sprays and baits can help kill some of the ants you see, but is unlikely to control the colony. Several species of ants require professional pest control, such as black carpenter ants.

❋   ❋   ❋

Ants can cause structural damage or simply be downright annoying. In either case, controlling their large colonies is best left to pest control experts. Your house is your castle and deserves protection from tiny intruders capable of massive destruction.

CHAPTER FIVE

THE STING OF SUMMER

Cindy was dreaming of summer. After a harsh, cold winter of long workdays, she looked forward to kicking back with a cold drink in her hand and having barbeques in the backyard. When summer finally arrived, it wasn't exactly what she had envisioned. Wasps were swarming the yard, making it impossible to enjoy the weather. I came out and found a lot more than burgers on the barbeque menu - wasps had made their nest inside the grill!

WASPS: DESCRIPTION AND APPEARANCE

There are more than 500 species of wasps. Most wasps are social species that live in multi-member colonies numbering from fewer than ten individuals up to fifteen thousand. These nuisance wasps include hornets, yellow jackets, paper wasps, and mud daubers.

Wasps range from 13 to 40 mm in length, are yellow, white, black, or reddish, and have three pairs of legs and two pairs of thin, transparent wings. Different wasp species bear characteristic markings. Unlike most bees, wasps are generally hairless. The body of a wasp is composed of three distinct parts: head, thorax, and abdomen.

SIGNS OF WASP INFESTATION

A common sign of wasp infestation is the wasp nest. These may be found in or around homes or other structures. Different wasp species have different nest-building locations. Paper wasps create aerial nests, which can be found hanging from trees, under roof eaves, and from decking, arbors, and gazebos. In contrast, most yellow jackets create underground nests, utilizing former rodent burrows or cavities beneath rocks and shrubs. Wasps are aggressive and readily defend their nests by stinging any perceived threats. Individuals with allergies to wasp venom may experience debilitating and potentially life-threatening reactions if stung.

WASP HABITATS

Different wasp species construct nests that range in shape, size, and location. In the case of paper wasps, nests are built using a thin, paper-like material that is created when the wasps chew plant materials and glue them back together. The nests of paper wasps consist of 150 to 300 cells arranged in a single comb-like layer, and the nests have stalks or stems called a pedicel. Paper wasps typically attach their nests to fences, tree branches, roof eaves, frames of doors and windows, and exterior trim.

Like paper wasps, the nests of yellow jackets and hornets are constructed of plant materials. These nests comprise 1,500 to 3,500 cells arranged in several layers, consist of five to nine combs, and may be enclosed in a paper envelope or not enveloped. Some yellow jacket nests can be quite large and similar in size to a soccer ball. Hornets and yellow jackets commonly create nests in hollow trees, wall voids, and the interiors of outbuildings, whereas other nests may be located underground in areas free of vegetation. Unlike other social wasps, mud daubers are a solitary wasp species. The mud daubers' name is derived from the nests they construct from mud. These nests are around 20 to 25 mm long and are built next to one another to form clusters up to 120 mm wide. Mud daubers prefer sheltered areas for nesting sites, such as exterior trim and outbuildings.

THE DIET OF A WASP

Wasps feed on plant materials such as nectar, fruit juices, or honeydew. Many common wasp species are primarily scavengers or carnivores that specialize in feeding on other insects. As such, wasps play a beneficial role due to their predation of insect pests in gardens and crop fields. The scavenging behavior of wasps contributes to their interest in human environments and activities where food is located, which makes wasps common household nuisance pest insects.

THE LIFE CYCLE OF A WASP

As wasps develop from eggs into adults, their bodies transform through metamorphosis, which takes around six weeks for most wasp species. For the first few weeks after the eggs hatch, wasp larvae emerge to feed on dead insects provided to the larvae by stinging female workers. Next, larvae enter the pupae stage, in which the larvae transform into adult wasps over a few more weeks. The queen generally produces workers only at the beginning of the warm season, and those workers will then care for larvae while the queen lays more eggs. The largest population of a wasp colony occurs during the late summer to early fall. At this time, the colony produces reproductive generations of males and females. Shortly after mating, the males die, while the remainder of the colony dies off over subsequent weeks as temperatures decrease. Queens (fertilized females) overwinter and, when spring arrives, will lay the eggs that begin a new colony for that season. Queens prefer to hibernate in low-traffic areas of homes and structures, such as attics, outbuildings, or other storage spaces they can access.

WASP PREVENTION TIPS

- ✓ When eating outdoors, keep food items covered at all times.
- ✓ Keep garbage cans tightly sealed.
- ✓ Regularly inspect the home and yard to detect newly created nests early.
- ✓ Seal cracks and crevices that may be wasps' potential points of entry.
- ✓ Repair cracks in the perimeters of windows and doors.
- ✓ Caulk cracks along walls or baseboard voids.
- ✓ Limit potential food sources.
- ✓ Inspect exterior trim and lighting fixtures.
- ✓ Keep window screens in good repair. Wasps may use an opening of more than 6 mm to gain entry into a structure.
- ✓ Control populations of flies, ants, and spiders in and around the home.
- ✓ Promptly clean up food crumbs and spilled liquids.
- ✓ Store garbage bins at least 15 meters away from the home or outdoor activity site.
- ✓ Trim vegetation away from the exterior of structures.
- ✓ Discard old wasp nests that are no longer in use.

Q: Why do I have wasps?

A: Wasps are attracted to human environments and activities primarily due to the presence of food or garbage. Overwintering queens may seek out low-traffic areas of homes and structures, such as attics, outbuildings, or other storage spaces. Previously used animal burrows outside the home can provide suitable nesting sites and may therefore attract wasps to the property. Additionally, wasps may nest in bare or sandy soil, within wall voids, abandoned vehicles, or tree cavities found near the home or around the property.

Q: How worried should I be about wasps?

A: Wasps play a beneficial role because they prey on pest insects that can damage crops or gardens. Wasps can also deliver multiple stings when provoked, which could potentially result in deadly anaphylactic shock in allergic individuals who do not receive prompt treatment. Because wasps are highly territorial and can be dangerous and aggressive, the removal of wasp nests should be completed by a trusted and reputable pest control company.

• • •

Due to the aggressive nature of wasps, they can turn a summer of fun into one of fear. Many outdoor structures where you plan to spend your leisure hours serve as perfect nest sites for wasps. Take the sting out of your summer by consulting a pest control expert.

CHAPTER SIX

WHAT WAS SNACKING ON VICTORIA MANSION?

George and Karen had finally retired. At the ages of 91 and 87, they were looking forward to enjoying this next chapter of their lives in the dream home they had lived in for 47 years, Victoria Mansion. They found flying insects and discarded wings while relaxing inside their mansion but never thought much of it. They also began noticing mud tunnels in their beautiful maple wood floors. These trails were causing significant damage to the flooring, as well as to walls and ceilings. Upon arriving at Victoria Mansion, it didn't take me long to conclude that termites had caused many years of damage.

WHAT ARE TERMITES?

Termites are insects that feed on wood. Commonly, homeowners will encounter two types of termites: workers and swarmers.

Worker termites are 3 to 4 mm long and cream in color. They can often be found when one of their mud tubing systems or another source of infested wood is disturbed. On the other hand, swarmers are 4 mm long and either black or brown. Mature swarmers lose their wings, so homeowners can see them with or without wings. When you find discarded wings, this can indicate a termite colony in your home.

THE LIFE CYCLE OF A TERMITE

Since each termite is assigned a work role within the colony (soldier, worker, or swarmer), they have a unique lifestyle compared to other pests. The queen termite can lay up to 30,000 eggs in one day. These eggs hatch into larvae. After three molts, the nymphs reach maturity and are designated for their work roles. The swarmers (or reproductive caste) have the job of forming new colonies. Termites work and build the colonies until they die off.

SIGNS OF TERMITE INFESTATION

- Flying termites (swarmers)
- Discarded wings
- Droppings (which often look like piles of salt and pepper)
- Mud tubes
- Tunnels in wood
- Banging or chewing sounds
- Tight-fitting windows and doors

TERMITE PREVENTION TIPS

- ✓ Seal gaps where utility lines enter the home.
- ✓ Caulk around windows and doors.
- ✓ Reduce wood-to-ground contact, which is a common access point for subterranean termites.
- ✓ Keep a clearance space of 8 to 15 cm between the soil along the foundation and the bottom row of siding.
- ✓ Ensure wooden siding is greater than 15 cm above the ground.
- ✓ Remove cellulose materials from around the house.
- ✓ Inspect lumber, primarily used lumber or railroad ties, to be used for home or garden projects.
- ✓ Employ bug screens over attic and foundation vents.
- ✓ Apply a fresh coat of paint to seal the smallest cracks.
- ✓ Remove dead trees from the property.
- ✓ Stack firewood at least 6 meters away from the home, and raise the stored wood at least 20 cm off the ground.
- ✓ Inspect wooden fences near the house. Use a termite-proof paint or stain to discourage nesting in the fence.

Q: Do termites bite?

A: Termites do not bite people or pets. In fact, you will probably not encounter them very often unless a swarm occurs.

Q: What is a termite swarm?

A: Even though termites live underground, swarmers will use mud tubes to exit their nests, mate, and find new nest locations. If your house is near the nest site, these swarms can even enter your home.

Q: How long can termites live?

A: A queen can live for 15 to 25 years and lay an egg every 15 seconds! Soldier and worker termites have a significantly shorter lifespan, typically only one to two years.

•   •   •

Since termites can spread rapidly, your house may have many colonies by the time you realize you have an infestation. A pest control expert can help eliminate termites colony by colony to ensure that the house you have worked so hard to maintain doesn't suffer any more costly damage.

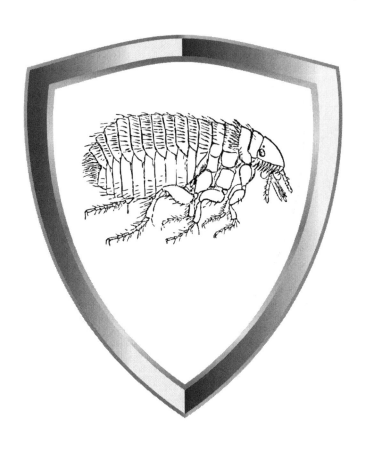

CHAPTER SEVEN

A SCRATCH FOR EVERY ITCH

My good friend, Joe, who I affectionately call "Tiny" due to his 350-pound size, lives on an acreage with his wife, three children, four cats, and two dogs. Joe began to get rashes all over his feet and lower legs, causing severe allergic reactions. The intense itching and shortness of breath were too much for Joe. He went to the doctor and was prescribed an antihistamine. Joe discovered tiny bugs hopping on the drapery, carpet, furniture, and even inside the kitchen cupboards upon returning home. When I received the call, I knew Joe was dealing with fleas. I advised him to take all of his pets to the veterinarian and headed over to begin the flea extermination process.

WHAT ARE FLEAS?

Fleas are tiny, parasitic insects. They feed on the blood of birds and mammals. Adult fleas are the only ones that bite, and they are known to feed several times a day. Fleas are wingless, flat-bodied insects that range from red to brown in color. They are 1mm to 4mm in length. Fleas are excellent jumpers.

THE LIFE CYCLE OF A FLEA

Fleas have a short life cycle compared to other insects. The life cycle has four stages: egg, larva, pupa, and adult. Adult fleas can live up to one year if an ideal host is present, such as a cat or a dog. A female flea will lay her eggs while attached to an unsuspecting host, where they will then fall to the ground until hatching. It takes 12 days for these eggs to hatch and enter the larva stage. The larva can take four to 200 days to enter the pupal stage, depending on the time of year. After the flea emerges from the cocoon, it is ready to search for a host.

SIGNS OF FLEA INFESTATION

On Your Pet:

- Hair loss
- Excessive scratching
- Pale gums
- Appearing agitated or uncomfortable
- Fleas or powdery white eggs in the fur

In the Home:

- Flea infestations commonly start on the carpet. Since fleas are dark in color, you can walk around with white socks to better determine the presence of fleas. In addition, fleas are attracted to light. If you shine a flashlight over a water bowl on the carpet, fleas will likely jump out of the carpet and into the bowl.

- Check all bedding (both human and pet). Fleas commonly feed on people and pets while they are sleeping. Flea excrement will appear as dark deposits, while eggs will be white.

On You:

- Check your skin for red bumps. These bites are mainly found on ankles, feet, and lower bodies. The welts will itch, swell, and have a similar appearance to mosquito bites.

✓ Cover children's sandboxes in the yard.

✓ Keep unwanted animals out of your home by repairing window screens or other openings.

✓ Maintain your lawn by mowing and raking, making it less appealing to animals that may carry fleas.

✓ Take the time to inspect your pets regularly.

✓ If you have cats, keep them as indoor pets.

✓ Ensure that each of your pets is treated with flea control products. Your veterinarian can recommend these.

Q: Why should I be worried about fleas?

A: Flea bites are severely itchy, but people and animals can also have allergic reactions to flea saliva, causing even more discomfort. Fleas can transmit diseases like typhus and parasites such as tapeworms. Most of us love our pets as much as our children, and pets can experience hair loss, overall agitation, and even anemia in severe cases of flea infestation. Flea bites can remain inflamed and itchy for many weeks, distressing both humans and pets.

• • •

Though at-home remedies are available, they are only a temporary fix. Fleas often reproduce in undetected areas. A pest control expert is highly recommended to destroy the entire population in and around your home. The old Ogden Nash saying goes, "Happiness is having a scratch for every itch," but I don't think he was referring to flea infestations.

CHAPTER EIGHT

WHO PLUCKED THE PEONIES?

Ashley was a flower enthusiast with a massive backyard. She took advantage of the space by planting colorful flowers to attract butterflies. In her sixty by ninety-foot yard were many herbaceous peonies. The butterfly garden brought Ashley much joy until one morning, when she found destroyed plants above and below ground. She found damage to her beloved flowers' roots, bulbs, and stems. In addition, she noticed holes and tunnels on the surface of the lawn. She called me in hopes of restoring her garden and pinpointing the culprit, which turned out to be none other than the elusive vole.

WHAT ARE MOLES AND VOLES?

A mole is a small mammal ranging from 4.5 to 8 inches long. Moles have gray or brown fur, tiny eyes, and long claws for digging through dirt. They feed on various insects, including grubs and earthworms. Since they don't eat plants, any damage that may be done to plants is accidental and can be blamed on a different pest; a vole.

Voles resemble mice but are rounder in shape and have shorter tails. They have a large pair of front teeth, brown fur, and a gray or white belly. Unlike moles, voles are herbivores and eat seeds, stems, roots, and bulbs of plants. They are active year-round and can be found in insulated tunnels under the snow in the winter.

SIGNS OF MOLE OR VOLE DAMAGE

Moles:

- Inspect your yard for runways, which are long, shallow tunnels on the surface of the lawn.
- Look for evidence of mounds. Mounds are deeper than runways and form a cone shape on the surface of the grass. Moles will often check the mound for insects.
- Open holes are rarely a sign of mole activity.

Voles:

- Check for tunnels and runways along the surface of the lawn.
- Voles like to make secluded holes under leaves and plants. Inspect your garden and areas with extra foliage for signs of vole holes.
- Pay close attention to plants for signs of wilting or turning yellow. This indicates that a vole has been snacking on the roots.

MOLE AND VOLE PREVENTION TIPS

✓ Keep the lawn mowed and tidy.

✓ Limit the number of ornamental plantings that provide food and hiding spots.

✓ Use copper mesh buried several centimeters in the ground to create a fence around the base of trees and other plantings.

✓ Control insects around the yard to eliminate food supplies.

✓ Use decorative rocks and posts to combat tunneling.

✓ Limit how often you water the lawn.

✓ Employ plastic netting to protect planted seeds and seedlings in the garden.

✓ Use raised beds in the garden to limit access to garden plants.

✓ Remove debris from around the yard and garden.

✓ Promote natural predators to control populations, such as hawks and owls.

Q: Why should I be worried about moles and voles?

A: Though moles can be beneficial by eating grubs, slugs, earthworms, and small snakes, the damage they do far outweighs the benefits. Moles and voles have been known to destroy gardens, parks, lawns, cemeteries, and golf courses. Even though moles do not eat plants, they can still kill them by disrupting the soil around the roots. Mole tunnels provide easy access for voles, and, as we have learned, voles eat all the parts of a plant, quickly destroying gardens and lawns.

Q: Are moles and voles dangerous?

A: Voles can bite and carry diseases such as rabies and tularemia. Moles and voles can also attract secondary pests to your yard, including mites, lice, fleas, and ticks. Especially if you have a cat or dog that spends time outdoors, the presence of moles and voles increases the chances of bringing parasites into your home.

* * *

Once moles or voles have staked their claim on your property, it can be challenging to convince them to go elsewhere. Not to mention, voles are elusive, making it impossible to tell how many of the little critters are contributing to the problem. A pest control expert can help make your yard an undesirable habitat, restoring the beauty of your flowers, plants, and lawn.

CHAPTER NINE

"WHO'S BEEN SLEEPING IN MY BED?"

Carla was a lawyer by day and spent the rest of her time in a beautiful house by the ravine. She had an east-facing balcony, where she played cello for hours. She enjoyed watching the various wild birds, including hummingbirds, that would visit the five bird feeders on her property.

One night, I received a call from Carla at 2:00 am. She was panicked and had taken refuge in her vehicle after finding an unwanted slumber party guest in her bed - a squirrel! This squirrel refused to leave the comfort of Carla's covers, so I made my way over to help her. There were several entry points where squirrels were accessing her home.

SQUIRREL STATS

Squirrels belong to the family Sciuridae. The red squirrel is the most common in North America. Squirrels are small mammals that grow from 10 to 70 cm in length, have red, brown, gray, or black fur, and have slender bodies with long, bushy tails. Tree squirrels inhabit dense forests and nest in treetops. Squirrels are well adapted to urban and suburban environments, where they often encounter humans and pets. Squirrels will often nest in and around homes and other residential structures. Squirrels build different nests: dreys (loosely woven balls of twigs, leaves, and grass) and dens (squirrels' year-round primary residences created in cavities). Squirrels in human-dominated habitats will frequently build nests in the attics and chimneys of homes. Nesting squirrels can quickly damage the building as a result of gnawing on wood and electrical wires and depositing droppings all around. Squirrel infestations are typically discovered when residents hear scurrying in the attic during the day.

SIGNS OF SQUIRREL INFESTATION

- Destruction inside the home or other buildings on your property, including torn up insulation and chewed electrical wires
- Outside damage to fruit trees, flowers, bird feeders, or landscaping
- Strange noises or scurrying inside of the home, primarily in the attic
- Squirrel excrement in the attic or garage
- Water damage to walls or ceilings
- Squirrel footprints

✓ Cover all openings and vents in the roof with hardware cloth.

✓ Examine eaves, soffits, and utility pipe openings since squirrels often make their way into the home through existing holes.

✓ If squirrels are already in your home, ensure they are out before covering entry holes. Squirrels can cause significant damage when trying to escape after becoming trapped in an attic.

✓ Wrap telephone wires or cables in PVC pipe to prevent squirrels from using them as bridges into your home.

✓ Cut tree limbs and branches that are close to your home.

Q: Can squirrels transmit diseases?

A: Squirrels carry parasites, such as fleas, ticks, and mites, which may transmit diseases to humans and pets, including tularemia, typhus, plague, ringworm, Lyme disease, encephalitis, and Rocky Mountain spotted fever.

Q: Are squirrels dangerous?

A: Squirrels may become aggressive when threatened, making trapping them dangerous.

* * *

Though they appear cute and fluffy, squirrels can cause damage to the structure of your home by chewing through wooden beams. They have also been known to cause fires after chewing through electrical wiring. Consultation from a pest control expert is imperative to prevent potentially life-threatening situations for your family.

CHAPTER TEN

HALLOWEEN IN APRIL

The Richardson family lived in Alberta, Canada, and spent a significant part of the year in Phoenix, Arizona. One year, they returned home from Phoenix to find cobwebs everywhere inside the house. In a matter of six months, their lovely home looked like it was decorated for Halloween in April.

Spiders are hunters, using their webs to trap other insects as prey. Once they leave a web to build one in a new location, dust accumulates in the web, and it eventually turns into cobwebs. When I arrived at the Richardson's home, it was clear that a spider infestation was present due to the shocking number of cobwebs in corners and crevices.

SPIDER FACTS

Spiders are not considered insects. Instead of having three body parts, they only have two: the front body section called the cephalothorax and the abdomen. They also have eight legs and eyes that are considered "simple," meaning they don't see as well as insects. All spiders are carnivorous and venomous, and even though many people have "arachnophobia," only a small percentage are dangerous to humans. Spiders primarily use their venom to paralyze prey. Spiders weave webs from silk, which is made up of strands of protein. Spiders make this silk inside their bodies and release it from their abdomens. Webs can be used to catch prey, hold egg sacs, or line the burrow.

THE LIFE CYCLE OF A SPIDER

There are three stages in the spider's life cycle: egg, spiderling, and adult. Female spiders can lay up to 3,000 eggs at one time. The egg sacs can be found in nests, attached to a web, or carried by the mother. Mother spiders don't protect their young, and predators will eat most of them before adulthood. The average lifespan of a spider is one to two years, with most only surviving for one season.

SIGNS OF SPIDER INFESTATION

- Spiderwebs
- Egg sacs that look like tiny white balls in corners or on spiderwebs
- A significant number of flying insects, since these are a spider's favorite food
- Spider droppings (small black dots that have a splattered paint appearance)

SPIDER PREVENTION TIPS

✓ Trim back shrubs and bushes close to your home's perimeter.
✓ Remove clutter from the inside of the home.
✓ Seal windows and doors.
✓ Since spiders prey on other pests, take measures to eliminate these pests from your home as well.
✓ Promptly remove visible, active webs with a broom or vacuum cleaner.
✓ Purchase sticky traps.
✓ Install yellow or sodium vapor light bulbs at outside entrances, which are less attractive to flying insects - a spider's favorite snack!
✓ Patch drafts with caulk.

Q: Where are spiders often found in the home?

A: Spiders have different preferences when it comes to moisture. Some prefer damp, dark areas such as basements and crawl spaces. Others prefer dry areas like high ceiling corners and attics.

Q: Are spiders dangerous?

A: Most spiders are not poisonous, and even if they have fangs, those fangs are typically too small to puncture human skin. The most common venomous spiders are the black widow and brown recluse. If you are bitten by one of these spiders, you will need medical attention ASAP.

* * *

A spider infestation often requires two steps: eliminating the spiders AND the other insects they feed on, making it more complex. Though most spiders are not harmful, I haven't met many people who enjoy encountering them in their homes. If you happen to have a black widow or brown recluse problem, it is crucial to contact a pest control expert due to the risks associated with their venomous bites.

CHAPTER ELEVEN

NOBODY LIKES A FREELOADER - SMALL NUISANCE WILDLIFE

David enjoyed the safe feeling of having a home security system until the cameras were activated every night. David would get out of bed and stumble sleepily around the perimeter of his home. He never found much, though there was a distinct smell that resembled marijuana. Could it be a bunch of teenagers up to late-night shenanigans? David finally caught a glimpse of a black and white creature on the camera and contacted me to come out and take a look. After finding footprints leading to a burrow under his front porch, I set up cages, capturing eleven baby skunks and their mother. This explains the nightly activity and pungent odor! I caught the babies first and gathered them in one cage, which lured the mother to come with them. For skunks, in particular, I utilize covered cages since they tend to spray more when frightened. The cover helps keep most of the smell contained. I then relocated the skunk family 25 kilometers away from David's home.

Skunks aren't the only small nuisance wildlife I have encountered. On another call, I met Wendy, who had heard noises inside her vents. At first, she just attributed the noise to windy days. But the noise never stopped, even when the wind died down. She decided to examine the outside of her home and found a large hole in the roof, right through the asphalt shingles. Peeking out of the hole like a window were a mother raccoon and her tiny babies. She had chewed through straight to Wendy's attic and made a comfy little home for her litter. Wendy didn't hesitate to call me to remove the raccoons to a more suitable habitat.

TYPES OF SMALL NUISANCE WILDLIFE

Skunks

The scientific name for the striped skunk is *Mephitis mephitis*. Skunks are small mammals, 50 to 80 cm in length, with black fur and long, fluffy tails, bearing distinctive white stripes that run along their backs and down their tails. Skunks have a well-known defense when they feel threatened: they spray a foul-smelling, sticky liquid that is persistent for days and difficult to remove. Skunks are adapted to urban and suburban environments where they may encounter humans and pets. They raid trash cans, gardens, pet food, and compost piles when foraging for food. Skunks are opportunistic omnivores (eating nearly anything), including rodents, eggs, insects, worms, and plants, taking advantage of human-derived food sources such as garbage and fruits and vegetables from home gardens. Skunks carry parasites such as fleas, ticks, and mites and may transmit rabies.

Raccoons

The scientific name for raccoons is *Procyon lotor*. They are medium-sized mammals that grow up to 95 cm in length and have gray to reddish-brown fur, with bushy tails bearing black rings and distinctive black mask-like markings on their faces. The front paws of raccoons work similarly to human hands. Raccoons are exceptionally well adapted to urban and suburban environments where they may encounter humans and pets. Raccoons will set up dens beneath decks, unused buildings, and outbuildings. When infesting structures, raccoons are detected when they make noise, such as scratching, rustling, squeaking, or other vocalizations, when they are awake in the evening hours for their nocturnal activities. In addition, raccoons create latrines near dens for excrement, leading to foul odors that indicate an infestation. Raccoons are intelligent and will readily bite, claw, and scratch if they feel threatened. Raccoons carry parasites such as roundworms, fleas, ticks, and mites. They may harbor several pathogens that can cause potentially fatal diseases in humans and pets, including rabies, leptospirosis, and giardia. The latrines created by raccoons also increase the health risks associated with an infestation, as many of these parasites and diseases may be transmitted through feces.

Opossums

The scientific name for the Virginia opossum is *Didelphis virginiana*. They are also referred to as possums. They are the only North American marsupials, meaning they give birth to live, underdeveloped offspring (called joeys) that finish their development in a pouch called a marsupium. Opossums are medium-sized animals up to 55 cm in length with primarily gray fur and may be streaked with red, brown, or black. Opossums have a long, pointed snout with a pink nose, prominent whiskers, black eyes, short legs, and long, hairless tails. Opossums are adapted to living in various habitats, including those found in urban and suburban environments. They are opportunistic omnivores (eating nearly anything), from vegetation, fruits, seeds, and grains to animals such as insects, earthworms, birds, and frogs. When their usual food sources are unavailable, opossums will consume carrion, garbage, and pet food left outdoors. They can cause problems around residences by entering buildings and searching for suitable denning sites. When they set up their dens, they can damage insulation and ductwork and leave behind droppings. They may also damage lawns, steal from gardens, knock over trash cans, consume pet food left outdoors, and threaten the safety of pets. Opossums carry diseases that can affect humans and pets, including leptospirosis, tularemia, spotted fever, tuberculosis, Chagas disease, and rabies. They also carry parasites, such as fleas, ticks, mites, and lice, that can be passed on to pets and humans. Although opossums often play dead when threatened, they can scratch and claw and may bite with their more than 50 sharp, serrated teeth. Trapping and relocation of opossums are illegal in most areas.

Groundhogs

The scientific name for groundhogs is *Marmota monax*. They are also known as woodchucks or whistle-pigs. Groundhogs grow up to 70 cm in length and have brown or gray fur, stocky bodies, and long, bushy tails. They prefer prairies and open forests but will invade neighborhoods in the suburbs when they provide plentiful resources. Groundhogs are omnivores (eating nearly anything). Their diet includes grasses, clover, alfalfa, dandelions, fruits and vegetables from gardens, and animals such as snails, grasshoppers, and grubs. Groundhogs cause problems around properties, mainly due to their digging to create burrow holes that cause structural damage to yards, decks, and outbuildings. Additionally, ground-hogs carry numerous parasites, such as ticks, fleas, lice, botflies, and chiggers. They may also transmit pathogens that cause diseases in humans and pets, such as rabies and tularemia. When threatened, groundhogs will bite, claw, and scratch.

SIGNS OF SMALL NUISANCE WILDLIFE

- Garbage cans that are toppled over and rummaged through.
- Noises coming from under your home or deck, usually louder at dusk or night.
- Noises coming from inside of your walls or attic.
- Brown urine stains with a strong odor on ceilings or floors.
- Gnaw marks from sharp teeth on walls or electrical wiring.
- Small, brown excrement around the home.

SMALL NUISANCE WILDLIFE PREVENTION TIPS

- ✓ Keep the exterior of your home in good repair, including the roof.
- ✓ Trim landscaping and trees around the perimeter of your home and fences.
- ✓ Cover exterior vents and openings with screens or chimney caps.
- ✓ Do not keep garbage cans outside. Use sealed containers with tight lids and only place them out on your designated garbage pickup day.
- ✓ Fill holes under stairs with concrete.
- ✓ Remove debris and food scraps from balconies.
- ✓ Keep windows and screens in good repair.
- ✓ Do not feed your pets outside.
- ✓ Maintain the lawn with frequent mowing.

Q: Why should I be concerned about nuisance wildlife?

A: All of the animals discussed in this chapter carry diseases and have the potential to become aggressive and defensive when trapped. They also cause structural damage to homes and other buildings, destroy gardens, and create a potential fire risk when chewing through electrical wires.

* * *

It certainly might be tempting to purchase a trap and handle these critters independently. However, doing this can result in significant injury or illness. Trapping and relocation of certain animals can be illegal in specific areas, and treatment plans must comply with the Fish and Wildlife Act. For these reasons, it is necessary to contact a pest control expert for proper removal techniques.

CHAPTER TWELVE

WINGED MENACES

Darryl was thrilled to finally cut the cost of power bills with his new high-efficiency smart house, controlled entirely by WiFi. The solar panels on the roof were sure to save him money. After about a month, Darryl found that he wasn't the only one enjoying the panels. Hundreds of pigeons were nesting under the panels, causing an unsightly mess of feathers and droppings. When Darryl called me, I came out to clean and disinfect the area, sprayed for mites, and installed a pigeon barrier around the solar panels. In similar situations of pigeons nesting and gathering on roofs, installing spikes is another effective method.

Sometimes pigeons aren't just a problem outside of the home. Another client, Wanda, was hearing flapping noises in the attic. When I came out to investigate, five pigeons were nesting in different corners of the attic. In this scenario, I removed all the nests and eggs before applying a disinfecting treatment, spraying for mites, and sealing all entry holes. Wanda's attic was no longer a pigeon hotel.

Though pigeons are often thought of as the #1 pest bird, we get many calls about other birds. One of these calls came from Angela, who heard noises in her bathroom. When I saw twigs protruding from her bathroom vent, I immediately knew this was a bird problem. In Wanda's case, sparrows had made a two-foot-long nest inside the vent. I cleared the nesting materials, disinfected, and sprayed for mites. Anytime we have a bird infestation, spraying for mites is part of the protocol since birds are often carriers. I installed mesh netting and a vent cover to ensure no sparrows or other pest birds inhabit the vent in the future.

TYPES OF PEST BIRDS

The types of pest birds you encounter will be dependent on where you live. Here are a few of the most common winged menaces.

Pigeons

The scientific name for the domestic pigeon is *Columba livia domestica*. Pigeons are also referred to as rock doves or rock pigeons. They are 29 to 37 cm in length and have a 62 to 72 cm wingspan. They have blue-gray plumage and iridescent throat feathers. Pigeons are common in urban areas. As the first domesticated bird, pigeons have played an essential role in benefiting humans, but in modern times, they are nuisance pests. Like other birds, pigeons may transmit potentially fatal diseases to humans and pets, such as toxoplasmosis, salmonellosis, histoplasmosis, tuberculosis, yersiniosis, and chlamydiosis.

House Sparrows

The scientific name of the house sparrow is *Passer domesticus*. House sparrows are also referred to as weaver finches and English sparrows. They are 14 to 18 cm in length and have a 19 to 25 cm wingspan. Males have bright black, white, and brown markings, while females have pale brown and gray feathers. House sparrows, as the name suggests, commonly live near humans, which helps protect them from predators. House sparrows may transmit diseases, some fatal, to humans, pets, and livestock, such as beef tapeworms, salmonellosis, toxoplasmosis, chlamydiosis, erysipeloid, Newcastle disease, and schistosomiasis. House sparrows are exotic pests that can cause problems such as destroying homes and structures due to nests and droppings. They are also known for displacing native birds such as tree swallows, chickadees, Eastern bluebirds, and tufted titmice through aggressive behavior.

Starlings

The scientific name for starlings is *Sturnus vulgaris*. Starlings are also known as common starlings and European starlings. They are 19 to 23 cm in length and have a 31 to 44 cm wingspan. They have a black bill that turns yellow during the breeding season and a glossy black plumage that becomes duller and is spotted with white in the fall season. Starlings were introduced to North America and are found in the southern parts of Canada and the Pacific coast of British Columbia, in addition to migrating into the Northwest Territories during summer. Starlings are a species of pest that cause many problems, from being noisy to transmitting parasites such as fleas, mites, carpet beetles, and bed bugs. They may transmit potentially fatal diseases to humans and pets, such as toxoplasmosis, salmonellosis, histoplasmosis, and chlamydiosis.

Magpies

The scientific name of the black-billed magpie is *Pica hudsonia*. They are also known as American magpies. Magpies are 45 to 60 cm in length, with a wingspan of up to 220 mm. Magpies have strongly contrasting black and white plumage and a long, tapered tail. Magpies are opportunistic omnivores (eating nearly anything), including the eggs of other bird species. They sometimes create underground food caches. Like other birds, magpies may transmit pathogens that can infect humans and pets, including the West Nile virus.

Woodpeckers

Woodpeckers belong to the family Picidae, members of which are found nearly globally. Woodpeckers are 7 to 50 cm in length and have a wingspan of up to 75 cm. Their plumage may be olive, brown, black, white, red, or a combination. Many species have a crest (tuft of feathers) on their crowns. Woodpeckers are named for pecking at dead or decaying trees, buildings, siding, metal, and air conditioners to forage for insects, create cavities for nesting or food storage, or communicate with other woodpeckers. Their behaviors are beneficial when consuming insect pests on trees. But the loud pecking may also be a nuisance and damage homes and other structures.

Canada Geese

The scientific name of the Canada goose is *Branta canadensis*. They are also referred to as Canadian geese. These are large birds that can be up to 110 cm in length, have a wingspan of up to 1.7 m, and have a distinctive black head and neck with a white "chinstrap", while the body and wings are beige to light brown. Canadian geese may carry pathogens that can infect humans and pets and cause diseases, including avian influenza, botulism, salmonellosis, duck virus enteritis, and cholera. They are loud and aggressive, with the ability to injure humans and pets when attacked. They can cause other problems, like overgrazing on lawns and leaving feces around buildings.

SIGNS OF BIRD INFESTATION

- Loud noise - large groups of birds produce a disruptive noise instead of pleasant chirps.
- Large groups of birds congregate on the roof or other enclosed areas of the home structure.
- Bird droppings
- Property damage is caused by birds modifying structures to make nesting spaces.

- ✓ Eliminate water sources such as filled gutters and birdbaths.
- ✓ Do not spread seeds, bread crumbs, or other snacks on the lawn.
- ✓ Keep garbage cans tightly closed.
- ✓ Stop using bird feeders if pest birds are becoming a problem.
- ✓ Eliminate roosting areas by trimming trees and plants around the perimeter of your home and roof.
- ✓ Install obstructions such as sticky glue or spikes to discourage roosting on ledges.
- ✓ Remove the nests of pest birds as soon as they are built.
- ✓ Seal any openings that would allow access into the home.

Q: Are scarecrows effective in eliminating pest birds?

A: Scarecrows, fake owls, and rubber snakes are often marketed to scare away pest birds. Though they may work at first, most birds just get used to their presence and continue to roost and cause damage to your home and property. Birds are more intelligent than you think.

Q: Why should I be worried about pest birds?

A: Number one, the droppings from pest birds are a significant cause of concern. Pigeon droppings, for example, can cause blindness if they come into contact with the eyes. In addition, these droppings can cause damage to the paint on cars. All pest birds have a high potential to carry mites, as well as a multitude of potentially fatal diseases that can be transferred to humans and pets. As a congregation of birds expands, so does the damage to your home and property.

• • •

When dealing with pest birds, removal methods must comply with the Migratory Bird Treaty Act and the Fish and Wildlife Act. A pest control expert is familiar with these acts and can offer the best solutions in accordance with regulations. Birds are boisterous in large numbers, and groups can quickly escalate in size. It is imperative to take action before winged menaces overrun your home.

CHAPTER THIRTEEN

THE WORST KIND OF DINNER GUEST

Jeremy ran his own construction company. He wound down after long days of physical labor by cooking himself dinner each evening. While his dinner cooled, Jeremy would catch up on invoicing clients and employee payroll. When he returned to the kitchen, a considerable amount of his food had disappeared from his plate! Since Jeremy was familiar with construction, he began surveying his home for clues as to who was enjoying his dinner. He found animal excrement but not much else. When Jeremy called me, I concluded that roof rats (rats living in the attic) were coming down through the vent into the kitchen - not exactly the kind of dinner guests you would like to host graciously.

RAT FACTS

Rats are typically slender (unless overfed), with large eyes, pointed heads, and prominent ears. They have long, sharp claws and teeth that must be continually used to keep them filed down. Though their long tails appear bald, they are actually covered by fine hairs. Most rats weigh 3 to 8 ounces, with a body length of 17 to 21 centimeters. Fur texture varies depending on the species, ranging from soft to coarse or even spiny. Colors also vary, including brown, black, and gray, with areas of white sometimes found on the underside.

Two of the most common rats are Norway rats and Roof rats. Norway rats are also known as brown rats. One of the largest rats, Norway rats, can range between 15 and 20 inches long. They feed on anything they can find, including eggs, small birds, plants, and invertebrates. On the other hand, Roof rats, also known as black rats, are slightly smaller with longer ears. They are more common in tropical climates or coastal areas. Roof rats eat seeds, fruits, leaves, stems, and insects. Once inside the home, they are especially drawn to pet food.

Though rats are primarily nocturnal in the wild, they can adapt to different sleep patterns in urban and rural environments, being active during the day and at night. Rats are agile and can swim, climb, and navigate narrow surfaces like branches and wires. Rats are omnivores, consuming fruits, veggies, and meat. Pest rats are opportunistic eaters, consuming almost anything available to them, including grains, seeds, and nuts.

Rats dig burrow systems for nesting, food storage, and shelter. These can be found next to structures or other solid objects around the home. Rats make large messes while constructing nests, shredding insulation, cardboard, or other soft material. Rat nests are often found under eaves, in attics, lofts, or even inside walls.

Part of the problem with rats is how incredibly quickly they reproduce. Rats can breed from five weeks old until the age of two. Females are fertile every three weeks. They can mate up to 500 times in six hours! A litter consists of 8 to 18 pups, and a female can have up to seven litters per year. Those little baby rats can add up fast, and so can the destruction to your home, not to mention your dinners!

SIGNS OF RAT INFESTATION

- Rodent excrement can be found under sinks, in drawers or cabinets, or around food storage areas.
- Scattered nesting material, including shredded paper, insulation, cardboard, fabric, or dried plant matter.
- Teeth marks on food packaging.
- Chewed holes through floors or walls, allowing entry into the home.
- Stale smells.

✓ Remove leaf piles and deep mulch around your property that would make ideal rat nesting sites.

✓ Seal or patch holes inside and outside of the home.

✓ Eliminate food and water sources.

✓ Use a container with a tight-fitting lid for kitchen garbage.

✓ Do not feed outdoor birds because this provides an additional food source for rats.

✓ If you utilize a compost pile, mix it up to cover freshly added food scraps.

Q: Why should I be worried about rats?

A: Rats can infect humans with diseases such as rat-bite fever, hantavirus, lymphocytic choriomeningitis, and leptospirosis. They can also carry diseases transmitted by ectoparasites, such as murine typhus, plague, and Lyme disease.

In addition, rats can cause damage to pipes, wooden beams and joists, and even soft concrete. Due to their long, sharp teeth, they can chew through electrical wiring, causing short circuits or fires. Rats cause damage to food storage areas through biting and scratching, as well as to the food itself. After all of that eating, they must urinate and defecate somewhere. Unfortunately, the chemicals in rat excrement can cause permanent damage to floors, walls, and other structures inside your home.

Q: How can I tell the difference between a rat and a mouse?

A: Rats are larger and heavier than mice. Mice tend to have much longer tails than their body size, while rats have shorter, thicker tails. Both mice and rats can be brown or gray, but rats can also be black. Size is the most common way to distinguish between these two rodents.

• • •

Most people are scared at the sight of a rat. But they aren't just unpleasant to look at. Rats carry diseases that can be harmful to the people you love. Their destructive nature rates high among common household pests, tearing up walls and insulation and chewing through electrical wires. A pest control expert can identify the points of entry, find nesting areas, and eliminate rats from your attic or walls without causing more damage to your home.

CHAPTER FOURTEEN

GOING BATTY

I've learned in the pest control business that pests don't care what time it is. I received a call from Melinda at midnight, frantic about a bat flying inside her home. To make matters worse, Melinda's husband feared flying animals, so they both ran out of the house in horror movie fashion. I stayed on the phone with Melinda, offering her strategies to contain and remove the bat. First, I asked her to isolate the bat in one room and shine a flashlight through an open window to try and entice the bat outside. The bat didn't fall for that one.

I continued to provide Melinda with motivation and courage, which our clients often need most in these situations. Melinda remembered that she had just purchased her child's butterfly net from the dollar store. As it turns out, that was the best $1.50 she had ever spent. After flying around the room for several minutes, the bat was tired and rested above the fireplace. I told Melinda to cover the bat with the net, gently sliding a piece of cardboard underneath (if you don't have a net, a Tupperware container will work just as well). Melinda was able to relocate the bat to a tree outside safely.

With any scenario involving a bat, ensure that nobody in the household was scratched or bitten. If scratches or bites occur, I always advise my clients to capture the bat, contact the local public health department, and have the bat tested for rabies.

BAT BASICS

Bats are mammals that belong to the order Chiroptera. They are 6 to 10 cm in length and have a wingspan of up to 27 cm. Bats have small, furry bodies with long, membranous wings and prominent ears. While bats are commonly believed to be blind, they can see but have relatively poor eyesight. Bats often roost on or in homes and other structures, where their droppings, called guano, can cause significant problems. Sufficient guano buildup can cause ceilings to sag and collapse, while the droppings stain walls and allow for the growth of histoplasmosis, a lung disease in humans. Bats can use their sharp teeth to bite when threatened, allowing for potential transmission of rabies, a disease of the nervous system in humans and other mammals such as pets. Bats can also transmit other serious conditions, such as Nipah, Ebola, lyssavirus, and Hendra viruses.

SIGNS OF BAT INFESTATION

- High-pitched squeaking sounds.
- Seeing bats in and around outdoor structures such as sheds or garages.
- Bat droppings (oval-shaped with rounded ends).
- Noises in the walls or attic at sunrise and sunset.

- Entry and exit holes in the home that are stained with black resin.
- Dead bats on the property.
- A strong scent of ammonia (present in bat droppings).

BAT PREVENTION TIPS

- ✓ Fill holes and seal cracks in walls, attics, roof eaves, and chimneys.
- ✓ Use peppermint and spearmint essential oils to deter bats.
- ✓ Install bat nets to cover large holes.
- ✓ Eliminate food sources from around your home, including garden fruits and insects.
- ✓ Install bright lights since bats are particular about their dark nesting areas.
- ✓ Place mothballs around the house.
- ✓ Use ultrasonic sound devices to deter bats.
- ✓ Hang aluminum foil or mirrors as bats do not like reflective surfaces.

Q: If I see one bat, what is the likelihood there are more?

A: The odds are very high that there are more. Since bats are tiny creatures, it is common for people to have multiple bats living in their houses without them knowing.

Q: Do all bats have rabies?

A: Not all bats have rabies. About 2% of the entire bat population carries this disease, but bats should still be handled with care. Rabies attacks the central nervous system, and the treatment requires a series of vaccinations. Seek medical attention immediately if you think you are infected with rabies.

● ● ●

As bat colonies grow, so do the piles of droppings they leave behind, also known as guano. Please remember that guano needs to be treated as hazardous waste because it contains fungal spores that lead to histoplasmosis in humans. Histoplasmosis is a respiratory disease that can be fatal. For this reason alone, consulting a pest control expert for disinfection and removal of bat colonies is highly recommended. Bats are protected in most states for some of their positive environmental contributions, so don't attempt to take matters into your own hands. Leave it to the professionals to keep you and your family from "going batty."

CHAPTER FIFTEEN

ATTRACTING NEGATIVE ATTENTION

Jimmy was a prominent political figure in his community. He frequently attended speaking engagements and other events, but unfortunately, he had swarms surrounding him (and I'm not talking about swarms of his supporters). Jimmy had a mosquito problem.

When I arrived at Jimmy's home, I quickly realized that his yard was a breeding ground for mosquitoes. He had an old canoe accumulating water, pet water dishes, and yard ornaments containing standing water. He also had tall grass, which mosquitoes are particularly attracted to.

Many people don't know that *they* can attract mosquitoes as well. Jimmy was always wearing a dark suit and his favorite cologne. As it turns out, mosquitoes are attracted to dark colors and aromatic scents. Jimmy also enjoyed a tall, cold beer after a long day, and studies have shown that drinking a single beer will make you more enticing to mosquitoes!

THE SCOOP ON MOSQUITOES

Mosquitoes are small insects that bite. They complete their life cycles in still or slow-moving water, laying their eggs on the surface. Marshes, swamps, clogged ditches, and puddles are common breeding grounds. Depending on the species, eggs can also be found in buckets, outdoor toys, potted plants, tarps, tree holes, and old tires. When the eggs hatch in one or two days, they look like tiny worms. With ideal conditions, the mosquito life cycle from egg to adult can take only ten days!

Female mosquitoes bite humans and animals to obtain the blood they need to produce eggs. These bites cause irritation and swelling and can even cause infection in those who are allergic to the mosquitoes' saliva. This is known as Skeeter Syndrome. Mosquitoes can also transmit malaria, West Nile Virus, and Dengue Fever. When you think about deadly animals, sharks, bats, snakes, spiders, alligators, and wolves come to mind. However, the mosquito is responsible for more human deaths than any of these. It's no wonder most people would prefer to avoid them!

SIGNS OF MOSQUITO INFESTATION

- Living in a humid area or having standing water on your property.
- Finding mosquitoes in shaded or dark areas around your home (mosquitoes prefer to do their hunting at night).
- Hearing a constant, high-pitched buzzing sound.
- Finding itchy bites on your body.
- Discovering mosquitoes in your kitchen near sweets or fruits.

MOSQUITO PREVENTION TIPS

✓ Eliminate sources of standing water on your property.
✓ Change the water frequently in fountains, rain barrels, potted plant trays, and bird baths.
✓ Fill in holes with dirt that contain pooling water.
✓ Maintain swimming pools with proper chemicals and filtration.
✓ Fill in any gaps in walls, windows, and doors.
✓ Keep window and door screens in good repair.

How to Avoid Mosquito Bites

✓ Wear long-sleeved shirts, pants, and socks.
✓ Tuck shirts into pants and pants into socks to prevent mosquitoes' access to your skin.
✓ Try to stay indoors in areas of dense mosquito populations.
✓ Use mosquito repellent.
✓ Replace all outdoor lights with bug lights. These yellow lights are known to attract fewer mosquitoes.

Q: Are mosquitoes dangerous?

A: Mosquitoes transmit at least three diseases, including West Nile Virus, Malaria, and Dengue Fever. The West Nile Virus can lead to severe complications within the liver and nervous system, encephalitis, meningitis, and paralysis. As discussed previously, Skeeter Syndrome is an allergic reaction to mosquito saliva, which is unpleasantly uncomfortable and leads to excessive swelling and even infection of the bite site.

Q: What is the most effective repellent against mosquito bites?

A: Experts recommend any repellent containing DEET. DEET interferes with the receptors on a mosquito's antennae, which detect body heat, skin chemicals, and carbon dioxide while hunting. DEET will deter mosquitoes from landing on the skin and biting.

• • •

Controlling mosquitoes requires proactive treatment from a pest control expert. Unfortunately, the problem with mosquitoes is two-fold because they can be attracted to your property and you. Not only are their bites an aggravating nuisance, but the diseases they can transmit are also a severe health threat. Humans are notorious for craving attention, but this is one type we can all do without.

CHAPTER SIXTEEN

THE TRUTH ABOUT DELUSIONAL PARASITOSIS

The following story is different from the rest but essential to include for awareness purposes. Delusional parasitosis is a rare psychiatric disorder characterized by the belief that parasites have invaded the body when none are present. It can be overwhelming and life-altering for the affected person and their family and friends.

We received a call from Rebecca, upset about her home being infested with bugs. She stated that these bugs were crawling all over her while she slept and biting her constantly. Two other people lived in the home with her, neither of whom were being bitten by any evidence of bugs. Rebecca asked that we come out to do an inspection. There were no signs of pest activity of any kind. Rebecca called our office for seven days, still seeing and feeling bugs on her skin. When we asked her to provide sample evidence, she presented things like pieces of dead skin and dust bunnies. At

this point, I started to consider delusional parasitosis. After referring Rebecca to a skin specialist who could not find any evidence
of skin infections or scabies, she was referred to a psychiatrist.

WHAT IS DELUSIONAL PARASITOSIS?

Delusional parasitosis is a psychiatric condition where people
mistakenly believe they have parasitic worms, bugs, or creatures
invading their bodies. It is most common amongst middle-aged or
older women. In some cases, it occurs due to a chemical imbalance
in the brain from other health conditions. Though it isn't entirely
known where precisely in the brain this happens, some experts
strongly believe that dopamine plays a role in seeing, hearing, or
feeling things that aren't really there. Illness and stress are both
known to increase dopamine levels in the brain.

SYMPTOMS OF DELUSIONAL PARASITOSIS

- ✓ A "crawling" feeling on the skin
- ✓ Numbness
- ✓ Itching or burning sensations
- ✓ Excessive scratching or picking at the skin
- ✓ Skin abrasions caused by scratching
- ✓ Use of chemicals to clean the skin
- ✓ Self-mutilation
- ✓ Use of pesticides or other harmful substances on the body

TREATMENT OF DELUSIONAL PARASITOSIS

Like other mental health conditions, treating delusional parasitosis takes time and patience. Sometimes it can be treated solely with talk therapy, while medications may be necessary. If you suspect you have this condition, please know you are not alone. Working with a trusted doctor and psychiatrist team and surrounding yourself with a family and friends support system will help restore your sense of comfort and well-being on the road to recovery.

Q: Can delusional parasitosis be confused with other health conditions?

A: Many conditions cause "crawling" feelings on the skin, numbness, and similar sensations to delusional parasitosis. These include drug and alcohol misuse, lymphoma, Parkinson's Disease, thyroid disease, anemia, kidney disease, scabies, lice, HIV, fibromyalgia, certain medications, and other nerve disorders. This is why it is imperative to have a complete exam performed by a trusted doctor to determine a proper treatment plan.

Q: Can a pest control expert help me determine if I have delusional parasitosis?

A: Pest control experts know the initial questions to ask when arriving for an inspection, such as whether or not other people in the home are experiencing the same crawling sensations, bites, etc. They also have an extensive network of other professionals they work with, like skin specialists and psychiatrists, who can help diagnose and treat delusional parasitosis.

SCAN & LEARN

If you can relate to any of these Major Pest Control
"stories from the trenches," please contact us
for a free online and phone consultation.

Phone: 780-906-0911
Email: Service@majorpestcontrol.ca

ABOUT JUN BUKHT

ASSOCIATE CERTIFIED ENTOMOLOGIST

Jun Bukht is a man who has an immense passion and empathy for helping all of those in need. He's a licensed Pest Control Operator, and one of Canada's few Associate Certified Entomologists with over a decade of field experience. He wouldn't be where he is today without his lovely and talented wife, Tibal Jannat. She's also a licensed Pest Control Operator and an environmental health specialist with a Bachelor's degree in Environmental Health.

Together they ensure their company is always focused on being efficient, thorough, and environmentally friendly. They also have a twelve-year-old son, Fyrooz Bukht, who had his parent's insect expertise rub off on him!

Their company, Major Pest Control, began in Alberta in 2019. Like most other successful companies, they started in their garage. Major Pest Control has now become the market disrupting juggernaut throughout Canada.

Phone: 780-906-0911
Email: Service@majorpestcontrol.ca

WHAT JUN'S CLIENTS ARE SAYING

"The real life stories, vivid explanations, and valuable tips have made this book a must have for every household. This book deserves 5 stars!"

—Sladjana Jankovic
Osgoode Properties

• • •

"Jun has provided expert pest control services on our site for many years, and there's no one I'd trust more to do it. His response time is second to none, he explains his findings, and he provides solutions. It doesn't matter what type of pest it is—cockroaches, mice, flies, etc. Jun knows what he's dealing with and helps us resolve the issue quickly and effectively. I believe anyone would benefit from his knowledge of pest control."

—Ben Harbak
Oxford Properties

• • •

"The difference between Major Pest Control and the rest of the pest control companies lies simply in their services. I work in an industry where you don't get to choose it but the announcement of pests comes as bad news as a declined transaction; confusion, embarrassment, and stress take over.

Major Pest Control is so responsive, so knowledgeable and so prepared that it's impossible to think of calling any other company, when "you know a guy" that does it all in that matter. Jun trained his team with knowledge about all pest life cycles; he's earned Associate Certified Entomologist certification; and lastly, he built his team with people that care: about the customer as well as the business.

Who would be so comfortable with such an extensive warranty if you wouldn't be so confident with the services you are practicing? You never have to do a warranty call."

—Maria Gijiu
Leston Holdings Ltd.

Manufactured by Amazon.ca
Bolton, ON